A YEAR
IN COLOUR

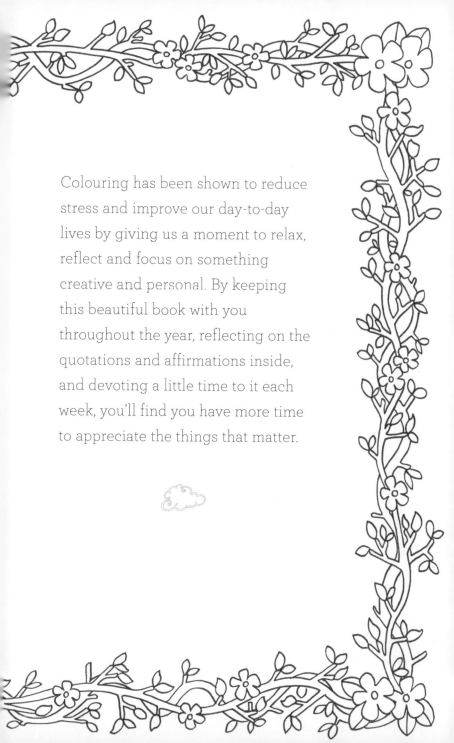

Colouring has been shown to reduce stress and improve our day-to-day lives by giving us a moment to relax, reflect and focus on something creative and personal. By keeping this beautiful book with you throughout the year, reflecting on the quotations and affirmations inside, and devoting a little time to it each week, you'll find you have more time to appreciate the things that matter.

JANUARY

Week 1

The most certain way to succeed
is always to try just one more time.

THOMAS EDISON

JANUARY

Week 2

Hope is a waking dream.

ARISTOTLE

JANUARY

Week 3

I ask not for any crown
But that which all may win;
Nor try to conquer any world
Except the one within.

LOUISA MAY ALCOTT

JANUARY

Few people know how to take a walk.
The qualifications are endurance, plain
clothes, old shoes, an eye for nature, good
humour, vast curiosity, good speech,
good silence and nothing too much.

RALPH WALDO EMERSON

FEBRUARY

He who is best prepared can best serve his moment of inspiration.

SAMUEL TAYLOR COLERIDGE

FEBRUARY

You make a living by what you get;
you make a life by what you give.

WINSTON CHURCHILL

FEBRUARY

Week 7

Three things cannot be hidden:
the sun, the moon, and the truth.

BUDDHA

We have all a better guide in ourselves,
if we would attend to it, than any other
person can be.

JANE AUSTEN

A lake is the landscape's most beautiful
and expressive feature. It is Earth's eye;
looking into which the beholder measures
the depth of his own nature.

HENRY DAVID THOREAU

MARCH

Week 10

Spiderwebs united can bind a lion.

AFRICAN PROVERB

MARCH

Week 11

Be still, sad heart! and cease repining;
Behind the clouds is the sun still shining.

HENRY WADSWORTH LONGFELLOW

MARCH

Week 12

While you are proclaiming peace with
your lips, be careful to have it even
more fully in your heart.

ST. FRANCIS OF ASSISI

MARCH – APRIL

Week 13

A loving heart is the truest wisdom.

CHARLES DICKENS

APRIL

You only live once, but if you do it right, once is enough.

MAE WEST

Don't walk behind me; I may not lead.
Don't walk in front of me; I may not follow.
Just walk beside me and be my friend.

ALBERT CAMUS

To be yourself in a world that is constantly trying to make you something else is the greatest accomplishment.

RALPH WALDO EMERSON

Not all of us can do great things. But we can do small things with great love.

MOTHER TERESA

Being deeply loved by someone gives you strength, while loving someone deeply gives you courage.

LAO TZU

MAY

Life is like riding a bicycle. To keep your balance, you must keep moving.

ALBERT EINSTEIN

Admitting you do not know everything
shows more wisdom than believing you
have all the answers.

My dear friend, clear your mind of cant.

SAMUEL JOHNSON

The will to win, the desire to succeed,
the urge to reach your full potential …
these are the keys that will unlock the door
to personal excellence.

CONFUCIUS

JUNE

Week 23

Do one thing every day that scares you.

ELEANOR ROOSEVELT

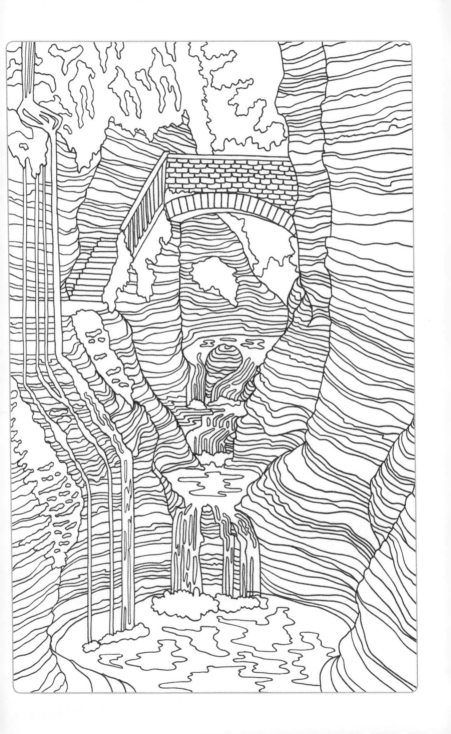

You have power over your mind – not outside events. Realize this, and you will find strength.

MARCUS AURELIUS

JUNE

Like madness is the glory of life.

WILLIAM SHAKESPEARE

JUNE – JULY

Week 26

To create a little flower is the labour of ages.

WILLIAM BLAKE

JULY

Week 27

Be yourself, everyone else is already taken.

OSCAR WILDE

JULY

Week 28

Every limit is a beginning as well as
an ending.

GEORGE ELIOT

Love should be unconditional; when you give it in this way you will receive it back in abundance.

JULY

Week 30

Time stays long enough for anyone
who will use it.

LEONARDO DA VINCI

Life without love is like a tree without
blossoms or fruit.

KAHLIL GIBRAN

AUGUST

Week 32

Try not to become a man of success,
but rather try to become a man of value.

ALBERT EINSTEIN

AUGUST

Only deeds speak. Words are nothing.

AFRICAN PROVERB

AUGUST

Week 34

The greatest prayer is patience.

BUDDHA

If you tell the truth, you don't have to
remember anything.

MARK TWAIN

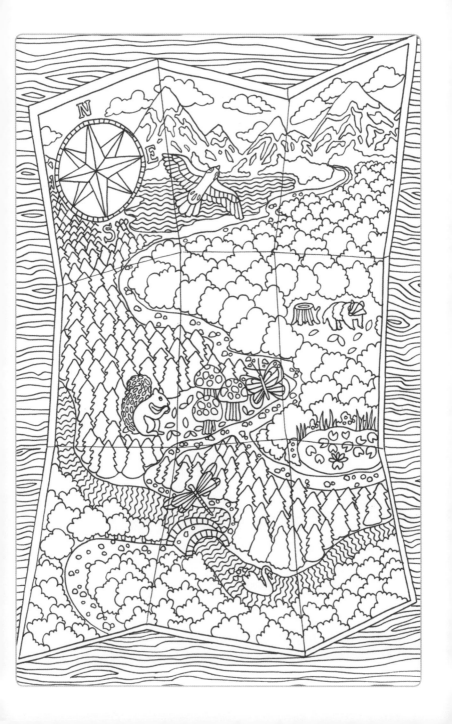

SEPTEMBER

The fool doth think he is wise, but the wise man knows himself to be a fool.

WILLIAM SHAKESPEARE

SEPTEMBER

Week 37

If you judge people, you have no time
to love them.

MOTHER TERESA

SEPTEMBER

Week 38

Folks are usually about as happy as they
make their minds up to be.

ABRAHAM LINCOLN

Be a master of mind, rather than mastered by mind.

ZEN SAYING

OCTOBER

Week 40

Be the change that you wish to see in the world.

MAHATMA GANDHI

OCTOBER

Week 41

There is no charm equal to tenderness of heart.

JANE AUSTEN

As a bee gathering nectar does not harm
or disturb the colour and fragrance of
the flower; so do the wise move through
the world.

BUDDHA

OCTOBER

Week 43

My true religion is kindness.

DALAI LAMA

OCTOBER – NOVEMBER

Week 44

The only way to have a friend is to be one.

RALPH WALDO EMERSON

NOVEMBER

Week 45

Happy is the man who has broken the chains which hurt the mind, and has given up worrying once and for all.

OVID

NOVEMBER

Week 46

I confess I do not know why, but looking at
the stars always makes me dream.

VINCENT VAN GOGH

NOVEMBER

Week 47

Correction does much, but encouragement
does more.

JOHANN WOLFGANG VON GOETHE

Life is 10 per cent what happens to you and 90 per cent how you react to it.

DECEMBER

Week 49

No kind action ever stops with itself.
The greatest work that kindness does to
others is that it makes them kind themselves.

AMELIA EARHART

DECEMBER

Any man that walks the mead
In bud, or blade, or bloom, may find
A meaning suited to his mind.

ALFRED TENNYSON

DECEMBER
Week 51

Share the kindness that's in your soul.
Even the smallest acts of generosity can
bring great joy to yourself and others.

DECEMBER

Week 52

Success is not final, failure is not fatal:
it is the courage to continue that counts.

WINSTON CHURCHILL

Published in the UK in 2015 by

Quercus Publishing Ltd
Carmelite House
50 Victoria Embankment
London EC4Y 0DZ

An Hachette UK company

A CIP catalogue record for this book is available
from the British Library

ISBN 978 1 78429 845 6

10 9 8 7 6 5 4 3 2 1

Designed and typeset by Carrdesignstudio.com
Printed and bound in the UK by Clays Ltd, St Ives plc

AMBER ANDERSON is a freelance illustrator from London, UK. Her work is almost always highly intricate: she enjoys capturing a sense of nostalgia and unusual environments in her illustrations. Some of her past projects include illustrating board games, shop interiors, clothing and accessories as well as working in commercial settings. She enjoys focusing her work on illustrating products that people can use and enjoy.